Gold Stars®

KS2 ENGLISH

Ages 7-9

Nina Filipek

Educational consultant: Ann Dicks
Illustrated by Rob Davis/www.the-art-agency.co.uk
and Tom Connell/www.the-art-agency.co.uk

First published by Parragon in 2009

Parragon
Queen Street House
4 Queen Street
Bath BA1 1HE, UK

ISBN 978-1-4075-3782-5

Printed in Malaysia

Notes to parents

The Gold Stars® Key Stage 2 series

The Gold Stars® Key Stage 2 series has been created to help your child revise and practise key skills and information learned in school. Each book is a complete companion to the Key Stage 2 curriculum and has been written by an expert team of teachers. The books will help to prepare your child for the SATS tests that they take in Year 6.

The books also support Scottish National Guidelines 5-14.

How to use this book

- Do talk about what's on the page. Let your child know that you are sharing the activities. Talking about the sections that introduce and revise essential information is particularly important. Usually children will be able to do the fill-in activities fairly independently.

- Keep work times short. Do leave a page that seems too difficult and return to it later.

- It does not matter if your child does some of the pages out of turn.

- Your child does not need to answer the questions in complete sentences.

- Check your child's answers using the answer section on pages 60-63. Give lots of praise and encouragement and remember to reward effort as well as achievement.

- Do not become anxious if your child finds any of the pages too difficult. Children learn at different rates.

Contents

Spelling, grammar and punctuation

Reading comprehension

Fiction

Non-fiction

Writing composition

Fiction

Non-fiction

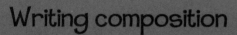

Look, say, cover, write, check

Learning objective: To learn different spelling methods.

One way to learn to spell a new word is by using this 5-step method: look at each of the letters in the word, say the word aloud, then cover it and write the word from memory - finally, you can check to see if you are right!

1. Look at the word
2. Say it
3. Cover it
4. Write it
5. Check it

You can learn to spell words in groups by looking for common letter patterns. Learn to spell these groups of words.

could, should, would

clown, frown, town

bridge, fudge, hedge

found, ground, loud, shout

coin, noise, soil, voice

cuddle, middle, little, table

A

Sometimes you can find a root word or a word within a word.
Underline the root word in each of these groups of words.

<u>cook</u>	<u>cook</u>er	<u>cook</u>ery
<u>spark</u>	<u>spark</u>le	<u>spark</u>ler
<u>clear</u>	<u>clear</u>ed	<u>clear</u>ly
<u>bedroom</u>	<u>bed</u>stead	<u>bed</u>time
<u>sign</u>	<u>sign</u>al	<u>sign</u>ature

> What is the difference between a dog's tail and a fairytale?

B

Here are some tricky spellings called **homophones.** They are words that sound the same but are spelled differently. Write these homophones in the correct spaces below.

hear or **here**	**ate** or **eight**
right or **write**	**beech** or **beach**
would or **wood**	**where, were** or **wear**

1. Teri is nearly _____ years old.
2. I couldn't _____ what she said.
3. I don't know if it's the _____ way.
4. _wher_ _____ you like to sleep over at my house?
5. _____ can I get the bus into town?
6. We made sandcastles on the _____ .

List any other homophones that you know:

DEFINITION

homophones Words that have the same sound but a different spelling and meaning, e.g. hair and hare.

Learn to spell tricky words by making up a mnemonic – a picture or a clue to help you remember, e.g. this **hear** has an **ear** in it!

Important spellings

Learning objective: To learn to spell frequently used words.

You should learn to spell words that you often use when you are reading and writing. For example, days of the week, months of the year and words for numbers.

A

Write the names of the days of the week:

Today is _____ .
Yesterday was _____ .
Tomorrow is _____ .

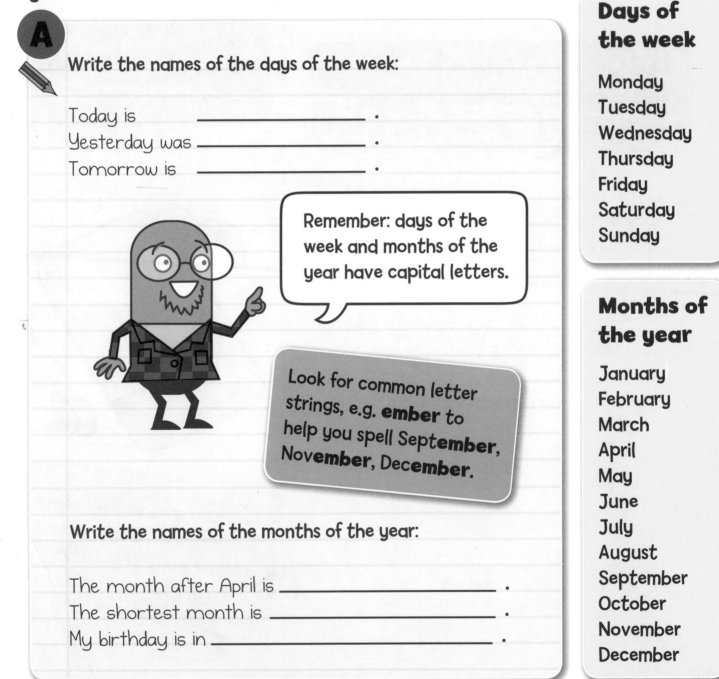

Remember: days of the week and months of the year have capital letters.

Look for common letter strings, e.g. **ember** to help you spell Sept**ember**, Nov**ember**, Dec**ember**.

Write the names of the months of the year:

The month after April is _____ .
The shortest month is _____ .
My birthday is in _____ .

Days of the week

Monday
Tuesday
Wednesday
Thursday
Friday
Saturday
Sunday

Months of the year

January
February
March
April
May
June
July
August
September
October
November
December

Don't forget that place names always start with capital letters.

Here are the words for the ordinal numbers:

first, second, third, fourth, fifth, sixth, seventh, eighth, ninth, tenth

B Write the ordinal numbers here and try to learn them.

1st _____

2nd _____

3rd _____

4th _____

5th _____

6th _____

7th _____

8th _____

9th . _____

10th _____

Learn to spell words that often appear in addresses. For example:

Street	Avenue	Close
Road	Lane	Drive

Cherry Tree Primary

Always use capital letters in postcodes.

C Write your home address:

Now write your school address:

Nouns and plurals

Learning objective: To learn plural forms of words.

A **noun** is a person, a place or a thing. Nouns can be **singular** (only one) or **plural** (more than one).

A

When we make most words plural we add an **s** to the end. Write the plurals.

sausage**s** cake_ drink_

book_ horse_ tree_

But if a word ends in **ch**, **sh**, **s**, **ss** or **x** we usually add **es**. Write the plurals.

dish**es** kiss__ fox__ lunch__

bus__ wish__ cross__

If a noun ends in a consonant plus **y**, we drop the **y** and write **ies**. Write the plurals.

pony > **ponies** baby > _____ story > _____

daisy > _____ cherry > _____ berry > _____

These words are very tricky because they don't follow the rules. You will need to learn these plural words by heart.

man > men child > children leaf > leaves
mouse > mice goose > geese person > people

B

Read the poem below and turn the singular nouns into plural nouns. Mostly you can just add **s** but sometimes you have to rewrite the word in the space.

I Love the Seasons

I love it in the spring when the **bud__** burst into **million__** of tiny **flower__** .

I love it in the summer when we can make **sandcastle__** on the beach.

I love it in the autumn when the **leaf _____** on the **tree__** turn from green to gold.

Best of all, I love it in the winter when we can make **snowman _____** .

The words **sheep**, **deer** and **fish** stay the same whether they are singular or plural.

C

Change the nouns in bold in these sentences to plurals.

1. There is a **mouse** in the house! › There are _____ in the house!

2. There was only one **loaf**. › There were only two _____ .

3. We saw a **goose** in the park. › We saw _____ in the park.

Prefixes and suffixes

Learning objective: To learn common prefixes and suffixes.

Prefixes are extra letters added to the beginning of words. They can change the meaning of the root word.

For example:

The rabbit appeared then **dis**appeared then **re**appeared!

A

Writing **un** at the beginning of these words will change their meaning. Try it and see!

untie	___fair
___lock	___do
___like	___lucky
___likely	___happy
___able	___hurt

Now choose three words from the lists above to complete the dialogue below. Write the words in the spaces.

Tom's mum: I'm very _____ with you.

Tom: It's so _____! It wasn't my fault.

I'm just _____!

DEFINITION

prefixes These are the extra letters added to the beginning of a word.

suffixes These are the extra letters added to the end of a word.

B

Underline words with prefixes in this passage. Look for **dis, re, im, un.**

Tom and Jez went to see a remake of *Monsters of the Deep.* Writing about it in a movie review for their school magazine, they said, "The monsters were unrealistic and unimaginative really. There was lots of action but the plot was disjointed and impossible to follow."

Suffixes are extra letters added to the end of words. Look at how these suffixes change the meaning of the root word.

The word **unsuccessful** has a prefix *and* a suffix!

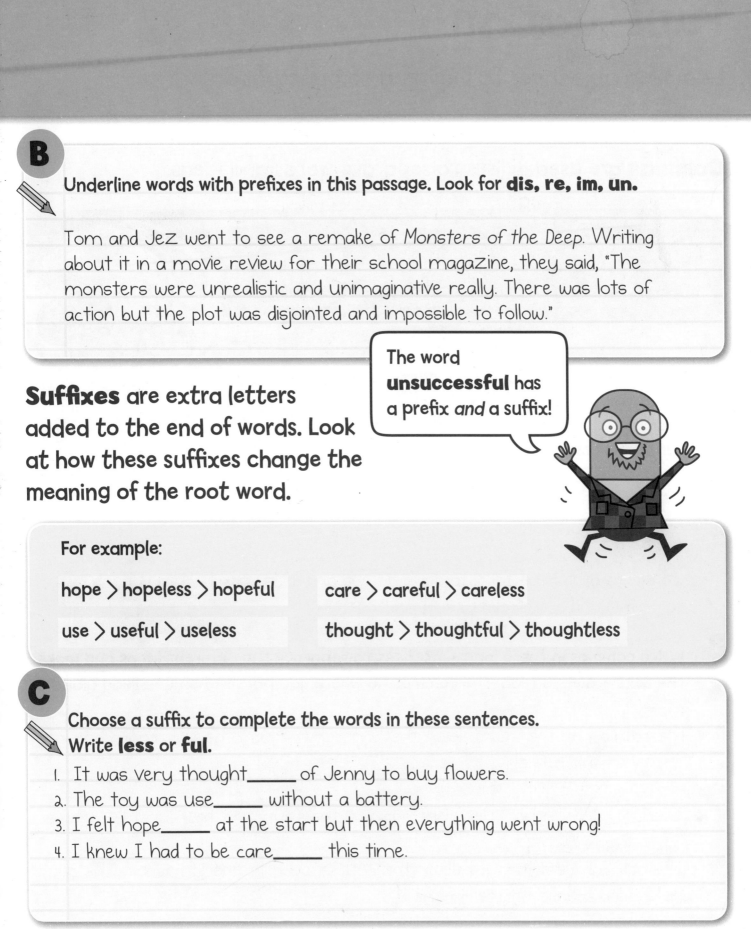

For example:

hope > hopeless > hopeful

use > useful > useless

care > careful > careless

thought > thoughtful > thoughtless

C

Choose a suffix to complete the words in these sentences.
Write **less** or **ful**.

1. It was very thought_____ of Jenny to buy flowers.
2. The toy was use_____ without a battery.
3. I felt hope_____ at the start but then everything went wrong!
4. I knew I had to be care_____ this time.

Punctuation

Learning objective: To learn basic punctuation.

Commas are used in lists to separate words and ideas.

> **For example:**
>
> The huge plate was piled high with bacon, egg, mushrooms, fried onions, black pudding, baked beans and tomato!

How to use commas:
- Write a comma after each item in a list.
- Write a comma to separate ideas within a sentence.

A Write the commas in these sentences.

1. We'll have two cornets with raspberry sauce a vanilla ice cream a carton of orange juice and a cup of tea please.

2. I'd like to order the tomato soup an egg and cress sandwich a banana smoothie and a chocolate muffin please.

B Write commas in these long sentences to separate the different ideas and make the text easier to read. The commas go where you pause when you read aloud.

1. The cat ran up the stairs down the corridor through the classroom and into Mrs Worgan's office!

2. Go right at the lights turn right again at the T-junction then first left.

3. The golf ball went straight down the course over the rough across the pond and landed square on the green.

Sentences that ask questions usually begin with **What**, **When**, **Where**, **How** or **Can**.

Exclamation marks (!) show surprise and excitement.
Question marks (?) are used at the end of sentences when a question is asked.

C

Read the sentences below and decide whether to write an exclamation mark or a question mark in each one.

1. Suddenly, all the lights went out__
2. "Aaaaaaaargh__" he cried.
3. Gina called out, "Hey, Tom__"
4. "What are 'gators__" she asked.
5. How do we know there's no life on Mars__

Speech marks highlight words that are spoken.

For example:

"How many children are coming?" asked Jason.

How to use speech marks:
- Open the speech marks at the start and close them at the end of the words spoken.
- All other punctuation goes inside the speech marks.

D

Write the speech marks in the sentences below.

1. Tara cried, Wait for me!
2. Do you think he's an elf? said Taylor.
3. Okay, said Sharon. What's wrong?
4. Wow! said Zac. You're a genius!

15

Apostrophes

Learning objective: To learn to use apostrophes.

Apostrophes can shorten words or tell you to whom something belongs.

An apostrophe can replace missing letters:

For example:

do not > don't   it is > it's

we are > we're   they will > they'll

Apostrophes are tricky! Keep practising until you understand how they work.

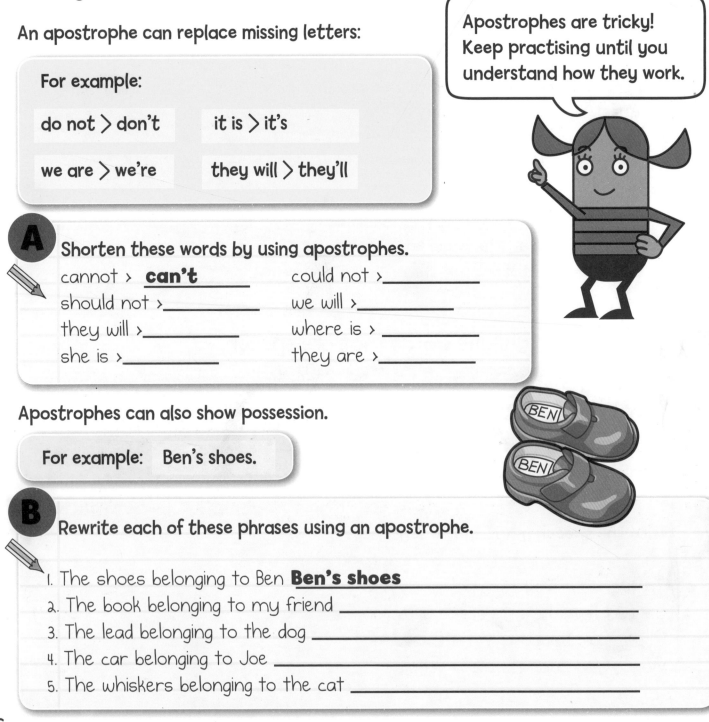

A Shorten these words by using apostrophes.

cannot > **can't**   could not >_____

should not >_____   we will >_____

they will >_____   where is > _____

she is >_____   they are >_____

Apostrophes can also show possession.

For example: Ben's shoes.

B Rewrite each of these phrases using an apostrophe.

1. The shoes belonging to Ben **Ben's shoes**_____
2. The book belonging to my friend _____
3. The lead belonging to the dog _____
4. The car belonging to Joe _____
5. The whiskers belonging to the cat _____

The possessive apostrophe can also tell you how many there are.

For example:

1. The boy's trainers were new. (one boy)
2. The boys' trainers were new. (two boys)

Remember these exceptions – the children's clothes, the men's clothes, the people's clothes.

If the noun is singular the apostrophe goes before the s.
If the noun is plural the apostrophe goes after the s.

C

Rewrite each of these phrases using a possessive apostrophe.

1. The fish belonging to the girl.

   The girl's fish

2. The book belonging to the teacher.

3. The television belonging to the family.

4. The red nose belonging to the clown.

5. The pram belonging to the babies.

6. The house belonging to the dolls.

7. The drawings belonging to the children.

8. The race belonging to the men.

Nouns, pronouns, connectives

Learning objective: To recognize nouns, pronouns, connectives.

A noun is a naming word. It can be a person, place or thing.

For example:

The bee buzzed.
bee is a noun.

Richard ran away.
Richard is a noun.

The cats miaowed loudly.
cats is a noun.

A Underline the nouns in these sentences:

The flowers were pretty.   I live in London.   The food was delicious.

Zak was asleep.   The girls laughed.   My sister has a laptop.

A pronoun is a word you can use to replace a noun so that you don't have to repeat it.

For example: Connor is kind. > He is kind.   **He** is a pronoun.

B Rewrite these sentences using pronouns.

Choose from this list: him   she   it   they   them   we

1. The flowers were pretty so I put the flowers in a vase.
   The flowers were pretty so I put <u>them</u> in a vase.

2. Zak was asleep so I didn't want to wake Zak up.

3. I like London because London has an interesting history.

4. The girls laughed because the girls thought it was funny.

5. Chris and I went swimming. Chris and I had a great time.

Noun A person, a place or a thing.
Pronoun A word you can use instead of the noun.
Connective A word that links ideas, sentences and paragraphs together.

Connectives are words that link ideas, sentences and paragraphs. Here are some useful connectives:

first, next, finally, consequently, later, suddenly, except, meanwhile, however, when, but, before, after, although, also, then

C

Choose connectives from the list above to complete this school diary.

Taylor's school diary: Tuesday

First , after register we had a spelling test. _____ we wrote animal poems. _____ lunch, we had a visitor.
It was Mrs White. She'd brought her new baby to show us.
_____ lunch, we had games outside on the field.
_____ , _____ it started to rain and we had to run inside. _____ , it was our science lesson. _____ , just before home time we had a story.

D

Now write your diary for yesterday in the space below. Choose connectives to link your ideas and sentences together.
Yesterday I woke up at...

Adjectives

Learning objective: To learn to use adjectives.

Adjectives are used to describe people, places or things.

For example:

a **large** dog

a **small** dog

A Sort these adjectives into three groups.
Write them below each group heading.

aqua	average	excitable
violet	sullen	bored
indigo	raucous	scarlet
huge	angry	ginormous
miniscule	lemon	narrow

Colours: Sizes: Moods:

aqua

B Write a similar adjective (a synonym) for these common adjectives.

1. We had a nice time.
   We had a <u>great</u> time.

2. The pizza was okay.

3. The giant stomped his big foot.

4. It was a funny movie.

Opposite adjectives are known as **antonyms.**

C Write an antonym for each of these adjectives.

black > **white**

bold > _____

hazy > _____

hairy > _____

unusual > _____

scorching > _____

expensive > _____

popular > _____

delicious > _____

polite > _____

D Change these adjectives to alter the meaning of the sentences.

1. A friendly, little dog came bounding up to her.

   A _____, _____ dog came bounding up to her.

2. It was an antique table.

   It was a _____ table.

3. It was a difficult job.

   It was a _____ job.

4. He was in a happy mood.

   He was in a _____ mood.

5. She went red when she saw him.

   She went _____ when she saw him.

DEFINITION

synonym A word with a similar meaning.
antonym A word with an opposite meaning.

Verbs and adverbs

Learning objective: To learn to use verbs and adverbs.

A **verb** is an action word. A sentence should have a verb.

For example: The alien **jumped** up behind them and **burped**!

A Underline the verbs in these sentences.

1. The mouse found the cheese.

2. The cat chased the mouse.

3. The frog leaped into the pond.

4. The boy ate the chocolate bar.

5. The card skidded round the bend and crashed.

Which sentence has two verbs?

B Change the verbs in these sentences to alter the meaning.

1. The girl dropped the ice cream.
   The girl _____ the ice cream.

2. The red team won the race!
   The red team _____ the race!

3. The family loved camping.
   The family _____ camping.

4. The children baked a cake.
   The children _____ a cake.

5. The boy ran across the road.
   The boy _____ across the road.

DEFINITION

verb A doing or action word.
sentence A group of words that belong together.

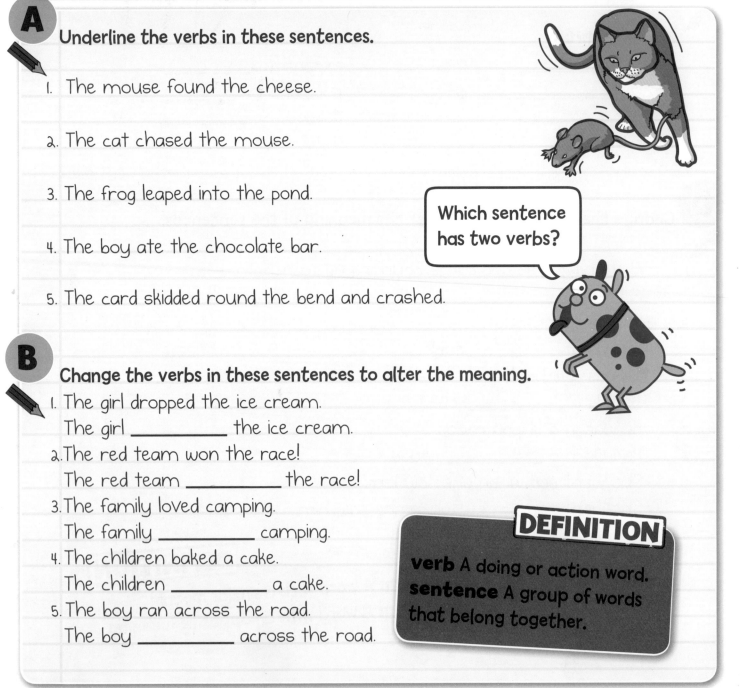

Remember: a verb is an action word and an adjective is a describing word.

An **adverb** describes the verb.

For example:

The alien **suddenly** jumped up behind them and burped **loudly**!

C

Underline the verbs in these sentences then circle the adverbs.

1. The cat purred softly.

2. The giant sneezed loudly.

3. The man drove quickly.

4. The sun beat fiercely.

5. She sang beautifully.

D

Change the adverbs in these sentences to alter the meaning.

1. The teacher spoke sternly.
The teacher spoke_____ .

2. The boy carefully wrote his name.
The boy _____ wrote his name.

3. The car quickly came to a halt.
The car _____ came to a halt.

4. The children played noisily.
The children played _____ .

5. I sneezed uncontrollably.
I sneezed _____ .

DEFINITION

adverb A word that describes a verb or an adjective. Many adverbs end in **ly**.

Tenses

Learning objective: To understand different tenses.

The tense of the verbs in a sentence tells you when something happens.

The weather forecast

Sat: sun		Tue: cloud	
Sun: rain		Wed: rain	
Mon: snow			

It rained last night.

It's snowing now!

It will be cloudy tomorrow.

A

1. What will the weather be like on Wednesday?

2. What was the weather like on Saturday?

3. What day is it today?

B Write the past, present or future tense sentences to complete the chart.

Past	Present	Future
It was hot.	It is hot.	_____
I was hot.	_____	_____
_____	He is hot.	He will be hot.
_____	We are hot.	_____
_____	_____	They will be hot.

24

To find out more about suffixes turn to page 12.

A suffix can change the time from the present to the past:

Present	Present continuous	Past
I play.	I am playing.	I played.
I work.	I am working.	I worked.

But look what happens here. When a verb ends in a vowel and a single consonant, we double the consonant before adding the ending!

Present	Present continuous	Past
I clap.	I am clapping.	I clapped.
I stop.	I am stopping.	I stopped.

C Complete these present and past tense verbs.

Present	Present continuous	Past
I paint.	I am paint____.	I paint____.
I jump.	I am jump____.	I jump____.
I shop.	I am shop____.	I shop____.
I skip.	I am skip____.	I skip____.

These irregular verbs don't follow the usual rules. You will need to learn them by heart.

Present	Past
I drive	I drove
I hear	I heard
I sing	I sang
I get	I got
I have	I had
I go	I went

Similes and alliteration

Learning objective: To recognize similes and alliteration.

When we say something is like something else, we are using a **simile**.

> For example: The rain is like a giant's tears.

This poem uses a list of similes to describe a cloud:

> **A cloud is like:**
> a smudge of white paint,
> a fluffy pillow on my bed in the sky,
> a white marshmallow,
> a blob of sweet, white icing.

Try to picture the sun as something else. The sun might remind you of an orange satsuma, for example. Write each idea on a new line.

A

Try to write a list poem, using similes, based on your own thoughts about the sun.

The sun is like:

I'm jumping for joy! Is that an alliteration?

Alliteration is when we put words together that start with the same sound.

For example: This monster movie is a massive hit.

B

Complete the magazine headlines below using alliteration. Choose words from this list.

DOGS   LONG   TWOSOME   LOCKS   TERRIBLE   RECYCLE   DRAMA

REUSE AND _____
DANCING _____ IN SCHOOL _____
TWINS ARE A _____ _____
LOOK AFTER YOUR _____ _____

C

Complete these sentences using fun alliterations.

My alligator   is called Albert   and he's adorable.
My bear   is called Baloo   and he's big.
My c_____   is called C_____   and he's c_____ .
My d_____   is called D_____   and she's d_____ .
My e_____   is called E_____   and she's e_____ .
My f_____   is called F_____   and she's f_____ .

DEFINITION

simile Saying something is like something else.
alliteration Words that begin with the same sounds.

Fiction and non-fiction

Learning objective: To distinguish between fiction and non-fiction.

Fiction books contain made-up stories. Non-fiction books contain information and fact. Fiction and non-fiction books are written in different ways.

Fiction books can have:	Non-fiction books can have:
• dialogue	• information and facts
• characters	• photographs
• a story or plot	• diagrams or maps
• illustrations	• an index

A

Label these book titles as either F for fiction or NF for non-fiction. Write in the box next to each one.

Volcanoes ☐   Poetry Collection ☐

Primary Science ☐   The Vikings ☐

Bedtime Stories ☐   Treasure Island **F**

DEFINITION

dialogue Conversation and words that are spoken.

index An alphabetical list of things in a book, with the page numbers on which each one appears, to make it easy to find things. Look at the index on page 64 of this book.

My book is called *Morris and the Aliens.* Do you think it is fiction or non-fiction?

Sort your books at home into fiction and non-fiction collections.

B

Read the texts A, B and C extracted from different books and match them to the correct book titles below:

Disappearing Worlds   Wizardy Woo   Secrets and Spies

A. It was on the night of the next full moon that things began to go wrong. Spells that had worked perfectly well for hundreds of years had suddenly lost their magic....

From title: _____

B. Supergirl sped past the secret agents in her souped-up spy car. She had to reach Point Blank before they did. Her secret life depended on it!

From title: _____

C. The world's rainforests are vitally important to us. But every hour, thousands of square kilometres of trees are being cut down all over the world.

From title: _____

C

Which of these books would be in the fiction section and which in the non-fiction section of a library? Write the titles in the correct columns.

Fiction   Non-fiction

Read the passage below and answer the questions about it.

Sale starts today

Anxious faces peer in through the shop window.

Inside, the manager's face is showing the wrinkles of someone twice her age as she frowns while fixing the last 'SALE!' sign on the rack. It keeps falling off and her fumbling fingers hurriedly tape it back in place.

As the masses gather outside, like hyenas to a carcass, the shop assistants stare meekly out and dread the opening to come.

The manager straightens out the creases from her suit and gulps before buttoning her jacket and walking towards the doors. With each step she feels like an underwater swimmer moving against the current.

Click! The key opens the latch and she is pushed back like a leaf carried in a storm as a wave of people stampede into the shop. The doors slam open, the chaos begins.

Remember: a simile is when we say that something is like something else.

A Use the text opposite to answer the questions.

1. What do you think the story is about?

   I think it is about sale in a shop.

2. Who is waiting outside the shop?

   The people (that want to go inside the shop (the custurmers).

3. How do you think the manager is feeling?

   I think the manager felt sad because he is fixing the last "sale" sign on the rack.

4. What simile is used to describe the masses gathered outside?

   "like hyenas to a carcass".

5. Which two similes are used to describe the manager?

   "With each step she feels an under water swimer moring against the current.

6. What chaos is about to begin?

   The people are fitting to go inside.

7. Write an alternative title for the story.

   The Toy sale

Fables

Learning objective: To learn to predict text in sentences.

A fable is a short story with a moral lesson. The characters in fables are often animals.

A In Aesop's fable of 'The Dog and His Bone', as retold below, some words have been left out. Predict what the words might be and write them in the spaces.

A dog was hurrying home with a big bone _____ the butcher had given him. He growled at everyone _____ passed, worried that they might try to steal it _____ him. He planned to bury the bone in the _____ and eat it later.

As he crossed a bridge _____ a stream, the dog happened to look down into _____ water. There he saw another dog with a much _____ bone. He didn't realize he was looking at his _____ reflection! He growled at the other dog and it _____ back.

The greedy dog wanted that bone, too, and _____ snapped at the dog in the water. But then _____ own big bone fell into the stream with a _____ , and quickly sank out of sight. Then he realized _____ foolish he had been.

Who was Aesop?

Aesop was a famous Greek writer of fables, who lived over two thousand years ago.

Research some other Aesop's fables at your local library.

B

Use the text opposite to answer the questions.

1. Why was the dog hurrying home?

2. Why did the other dog growl back?

3. What lesson do you think the dog learned?

4. What is the moral of the fable? Tick the correct answer, a, b or c.
   a) Waste not want not.
   b) It is foolish to be greedy.
   c) Be happy with how you look.

5. If you rewrote the fable using the same moral but a different animal character, which animal would you choose? Say why.

DEFINITION

moral lesson A lesson in good or bad behaviour.

Classic poetry

Learning objective: To understand different types of poems.

Read this extract from 'The Pied Piper of Hamelin' by Robert Browning.

Rats!
They fought the dogs, and killed the cats,
And bit the babies in the cradles,
And ate the cheeses out of the vats,
And licked the soup from the cook's own ladles,
Split open the kegs of salted sprats,
Made nests inside men's Sunday hats,
And even spoiled the women's chats,
By drowning their speaking
With shrieking and squeaking
In fifty different sharps and flats.

A

Now answer the questions.

1. What is the extract about?

2. Look at the first three lines. Which words are alliterations – that is, begin with the same sounds?

3. Find five words in the poem that rhyme with **cats**.

4. What is a **ladle**?

5. How many cooks are there? What does the apostrophe in **cook's** tell us?

6. Why do you think the poet chose these three words: **speaking**, **shrieking** and **squeaking**?

7. What are **Sunday hats**?

8. What does the poet mean by **sharps** and **flats**?

9. If you've heard the story of the Pied Piper of Hamelin, write down what you know about it. If you're not familiar with the story, try to find a library copy.

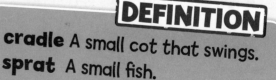

DEFINITION

cradle A small cot that swings.
sprat A small fish.

Nonsense poems and limericks

Learning objective: To understand different types of poems.

This nonsense poem tells a cautionary tale. Read it and then answer the questions below.

The Vulture
The Vulture eats between his meals
And that's the reason why
He very, very rarely feels
As well as you and I.

His eye is dull, his head is bald,
His neck is growing thinner.
Oh! what a lesson for us all
To only eat at dinner!

Hilaire Belloc

A

1. What sound is repeated three times in the first line?

2. Why did the poet choose the word **thinner**?

3. What lesson is the poet telling us?

4. Do you think this is a serious poem? Explain your answer.

Read the limerick below and answer the questions.

There was a young lady of Twickenham
Whose boots were too tight to walk quickenham.
She bore them awhile,
But at last, at a stile,
She pulled them both off and was sickenham.

Anon

DEFINITION

nonsense poem A poem that doesn't make sense.
limerick A five-line comic poem with a rhyme pattern.
anon Anonymous. It means that we don't know who wrote the poem because it was written a long time ago.

B

1. Why has the poet made up the words **quickenham** and **sickenham**?

2. What does **she bore them awhile** mean?

3. Write down a limerick that you know or make up one of your own.

37

Playscripts

Learning objective: To understand how to read a playscript.

Read the playscript below.

Scene 1: A New Puppy
Two dogs talking in the park.
Characters:
  Buster: Bulldog
  Sindy: Yorkshire Terrier

BUSTER: (wailing) A new puppy! After everything I've done for them.

SINDY: I knew you'd be upset. I said to our Mindy when I heard.

BUSTER: I take them for lovely walks, I eat up all their leftovers – even that takeaway muck they always dish out on a Friday… and this is the thanks I get!

SINDY: (sympathetically) You can choose your friends but you can't choose your owners.

BUSTER: What can they want a puppy for anyway?

SINDY: Well, puppies are cute.

BUSTER: Cute! Aren't I cute enough for them?

SINDY: Er…

BUSTER: Well, I'm telling you now. It's not getting its paws on my toys. I've buried them all!

How to write a **playscript**:
- Write the speaker's name first.
- Write each speaker on a new line.
- Describe how things are said, e.g. using adverbs in brackets.

How to write a **prose story**:
- Start a new paragraph for each speaker.
- Speech marks go around the words spoken.
- Use different words for 'said' e.g. replied, cried, shouted, asked, shrieked.

playscript The text of a play. It includes all the words the actors would say on stage, plus a list of the cast and stage directions that help the actors to decide how to behave and move on stage.

A

Now rewrite the playscript as a prose story. Fill in the missing words.

Chapter 1: A New Puppy

"_____!" Buster wailed. "_____
_____."

"I knew you'd be upset," replied Sindy. "_____."

"I take them for lovely walks, I eat up all their leftovers – even that takeaway muck they always dish out on a Friday _____
_____!" said Buster.

"You can choose your friends but you can't choose your owners,"
_____.

"_____?" cried Buster.

"Well, puppies are cute," said Sindy.

"_____?" replied Buster.

"Er..." said Sindy.

"Well, I'm telling you now," said Buster. "_____
_____!"

Formal letters

Learning objective: To read and understand a formal letter.

Read these two formal letters and answer the questions.

> 6 Acorn Avenue,
> Newbridge,
> N16 5BH.
>
> Monday, 6 May 2009
>
> Dear Miss Grinstead
>
> I would be grateful if you would allow Becky to leave school early tomorrow afternoon. She has an appointment at the dentist for 3.15 pm but I would need to pick her up from school at 2.45 pm. I'm sorry that she will miss the last lesson of the day but this was the only time available.
>
> As Tuesday is homework night, perhaps I could take Becky's homework with me when I come to collect her.
>
> Yours sincerely
>
> Mrs Alice Kenwood

A

1. If Becky's appointment is at 3.15 pm why does she need to leave at 2.45 pm?

2. On what day of the week is Becky's appointment?

3. Why does Mrs Kenwood apologise for taking Becky early?

4. Becky thinks she won't have to do her homework. Is this true?

Mrs A Kenwood,
6 Acorn Avenue,
Newbridge,
N16 5BH.

Monday, 6 May 2009

Botchit Kitchens,
Dead End Lane,
Newbridge,
NO1 1N.

Dear Sir

I am writing to complain about your company's shoddy workmanship on my recently fitted new kitchen.

Firstly, all of the doors are hanging off their hinges. Secondly, the drawers have been fitted upside-down so we can't put anything in them. Thirdly, you forgot to make room for the sink! What use is a kitchen without a sink?

I want to know when you are able to put these things right. Please call me to arrange a time as soon as possible.

Yours faithfully

Mrs A Kenwood

B

1. Whose address is printed on the left-hand side of the page?

2. What does 'shoddy' mean in the first sentence?

3. What is the purpose of the letter?

4. From reading the letter, how do you think Mrs Kenwood is feeling?

Instructions

Learning objective: To understand instruction text.

Read the instructions for making a thirst-quenching drink and then answer the questions below.

Apple and Raspberry Refresher

Ingredients (serves 1):
4 ice cubes
1 tablespoon raspberry syrup
250 ml or 8 fl oz apple juice
thin slices of apple for decoration

What you do:
1. Put the ice cubes in a plastic bag and crush them with a rolling pin.
2. Tip the ice into a glass.
3. Pour on the raspberry syrup.
4. Fill the glass to the top with apple juice.
5. Decorate with thin slices of apple.

A

1. What other things will you need in addition to the list of ingredients?

2. Is there enough for two glasses?

3. Is it essential that you have apple slices?

4. The instructions include the following words: put, tip, pour, fill, decorate. Are these words nouns, verbs or adjectives?

5. Write an alternative name for this drink.

DEFINITION

recipe A list of instructions for cooking a dish of food.

Look at the recipe and read the instructions for making a chicken salad sandwich. Can you spot a missing ingredient?

Chicken Salad Supreme Sandwich

Ingredients:
bread
margarine
cooked chicken
lettuce leaves
tomatoes

What you do:
1. Butter the bread.
2. Put the chicken on the bread.
3. Spread on some mayonnaise.
4. Then add tomatoes and lettuce.
5. Then sandwich together.

This recipe is badly written because:
• The list of ingredients is incomplete and unhelpful, e.g. we don't know how much we need of anything.
• The instructions are not clear.

B

Rewrite the recipe in your own words. Try to make big improvements on the original.

43

Read the text carefully and then answer the questions about it on the opposite page.

The Spanish Armada

In 1587, when Elizabeth I was Queen of England and Phillip II was King of Spain, tension between the two countries was at its greatest. Elizabeth had just signed the death warrant for the Catholic Mary Queen of Scots and this was the final straw for Phillip, who was also a Catholic.

In 1588, Phillip sent 130 warships to invade England. But the English saw the Spanish Armada arriving and the faster, smaller and more agile English ships harassed the Spanish along the English Channel. The Spanish ships were in a crescent formation curving around the English ships, and the English knew they would have to break this formation to defeat the Armada.

So the English sent burning ships to sail into the Spanish fleet. The plan worked and the Armada scattered. The Spanish ships were large, heavy and slow to manoeuvre. The English ships were quick and had better cannons so they were able to inflict a lot of damage. The Armada tried to escape back to Spain by sailing north but bad weather blew the ships on to the coasts of Ireland and Scotland.

Only half of the ships that set out in the Armada made it back to Spain. None of the English ships were lost. Elizabeth saw this victory as one of her greatest achievements.

Information text is found in non-fiction books.

A

1. Why do you think Phillip was angry when Mary Queen of Scots was executed?

2. What does 'this was the final straw for Phillip' mean?

3. Why would a crescent shape of Spanish ships be a problem for the English?

4. How did the English plan to break up the Armada?

5. What advantages did the English ships have?

6. Where was the Armada shipwrecked?

7. Approximately how many Spanish ships survived the battle?

8. How many English ships survived?

Shape and acrostic poems

Learning objective: To write a shape and an acrostic poem.

Read the shape poem.

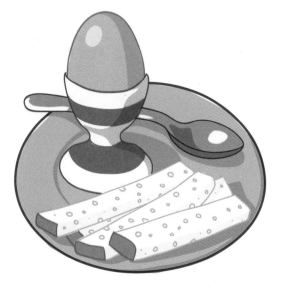

Egg
Yellow yolk
for my breakfast,
with dip-in soldiers.
I love eggy bread,
boiled, fried, scrambled,
or poached eggs... How
do you like your eggs?
"Made from
chocolate, of
course!"

How to write a **shape poem**:
- Draw an outline of a familiar object.
- Write your poem inside the outline, following the shape.
- Don't worry about rhyme - it doesn't have to rhyme.
- Try to include alliteration, e.g. yellow yolk.

This circle shape could represent a ball, a bubble, the Sun or the Moon - you decide. Then write a shape poem of your own inside the circle.

acrostic A poem or other piece of text in which when you read downwards some of the letters spell out a word.

This is an acrostic poem. The first letter in each line spells a name.

My brother
Always kicking a ball or
Running recklessly
CRASH! Into me!
OUCH! Look where you're going!

Here's another example:

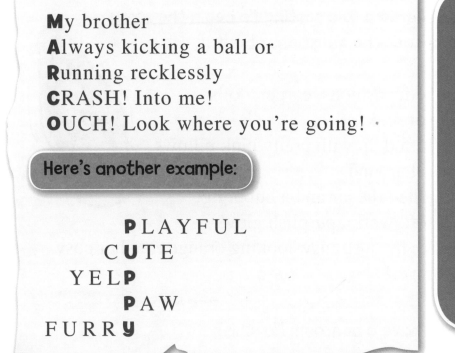

```
   PLAYFUL
   CUTE
YELP
   PAW
FURRY
```

How to write an **acrostic poem**:
- Write about something or someone that you know well.
- Spell out the subject of your poem vertically down the page.
- Alongside each letter continue with a descriptive phrase or word.

A

Write an acrostic poem of your own in the space below.

Settings

A setting is the place where the events in a story happen.

A

The story below uses a girl's bedroom as a setting to begin the story. Read the opening text and answer the questions about it.

> Everything matched: walls, bed, cushions, carpet, dolls – everything was either purple or pink.
>
> Her princess bed was fluffed up with pretty pink pillows and purple sequins sparkled all around.
>
> Rose-scented perfume filled the air and a bubbling, purple lava lamp gave off a soft, warm, purplish glow.
>
> But the day a friend gave her a strange-looking orange ring her cosy, pink world would change forever!

1. What sort of a person would have a bedroom like this?

2. Circle any alliterations that you spot in the second paragraph.
3. What do you think she thought when her friend gave her an orange ring?

4. Do you think the ring is going to be important in the story? Say why.

Say this tongue twister:
Princess was pretty in pink!

Writers often set their stories in places that are known to them. They might be places they've visited on holiday, where they've gone to school or worked. But sometimes writers use historical settings, especially if they have an interest in history.

B

Think about a place that is well known to you. For example, it could be your bedroom, classroom or friend's room.

Write words that describe what you...
see:
hear:
feel:
smell:
taste:

Now use your notes to write a short description.

How to write a description of a place:
• Try to imagine you are there.
• Try to concentrate on the picture in your mind.
• Write down your ideas in a clear order.
• Use powerful adjectives.

Characters

Learning objective: To write a character description.

Read the character descriptions and answer the questions below.

1. Grandpa Bob, old and gnarled, like an ancient oak, sits rooted in his armchair, surrounded by his books. Age has not dulled his sense of humour or his mind, which is still as sharp and clear as ever.

2. Auntie Deera was round and plump with a soft, sunny face. When she laughed, which was often, her tummy laughed too. Her favourite saying was, "You'll never guess what happened to me today…"

3. Zak was a terrible two-year-old and a tearaway at ten. Every day at primary school, his cheeky grin got him into and out of mischief. "It wasn't me!" he'd say.

4. Charlie's blue eyes are outlined with thick, black mascara. A skull tattoo on her arm makes her look hard but I know she's not.

A

1. Which of the characters is more likely to read books: Auntie Deera or Grandpa Bob?

2. Which of the characters is most likely to enjoy food? Say why.

3. Rewrite the description of Auntie Deera using opposite adjectives to change her character.
   Auntie Deera was _____ and _____ with a _____ , _____ face.

4. Which of the characters is the youngest? Say why.

5. How old do you think Charlie is?

Try writing a description of me! What adjectives would you use?

B

Write a character description for each of these people. Use powerful adjectives to describe their personalities and what they look like.

Miss Hanson, teacher

Bulky Bazza, weightlifter

Taz Tucker, best friend

A.T., alien being

Write a character description of someone that you know well. If you want to you can disguise their identity by changing their name, as many writers do!

How to write a character description:
• Choose names carefully because they suggest a character, e.g. Mrs Jolly.
• Ask yourself questions, e.g. What's their personality? What do they like to do?
• Different characters should speak differently, e.g. they might have favourite sayings.
• Give your character an unusual feature, e.g. eyes of different colours.

Story plans and plots

Learning objective: To learn how to plan a story.

Now it's time to write your own story. Can't think of anything to write? Don't worry, here are some ideas to try:

1. Think about all the books you have read. Choose your favourite and imitate it to help you write your own story, by changing the setting, the characters and the events.

> **For example:** you could write a story based on The Three Billy Goats Gruff but change the troll to a bully and the Billy Goats Gruff to you and your friends!
>
> I was walking home from school with Gaz and Tim when we saw him, swinging on the gate.

2. Retell something that has happened to you but change the characters and/or the setting.

> **For example:** write a story based on a time when you lost something. Perhaps you lost something very valuable belonging to someone else!
>
> Where could it have gone? I'm in big trouble now. Mum doesn't even know I had it!

3. Mix up themes from different stories. Common story themes are: good versus evil, friendship, kindness, something lost, a long journey, rags to riches.

> **For example:** write a story that explores two themes – friendship and rags to riches.
>
> Cindy carried her empty suitcase to the station. She pretended it was heavy so that the others wouldn't know she had nothing to put in it.

Whatever happens in your story, the characters should be changed by it in some way. For example, an evil character might see the error of his or her ways and become a good person.

Don't try to write your story without first making a plan. Your plan might be a spider diagram, a storyboard or a written list. Look at these plans for a retelling of the Three Billy Goats Gruff.

The Troll and the Three Billy Goats (retold)

Storyboard

| Billy goats teasing troll | Troll lonely | Small billy goat falls |
| Troll saves him | Making friends | Troll is happy |

List

1. Billy Goats tease Troll.
2. Troll is lonely.
3. Smallest Billy Goat falls off the bridge.
4. Troll saves him.
5. Billy Goats make friends with Troll.
6. Now Troll is happy.

Spider diagram

6. Troll is happy
1. Billy Goats tease Troll
5. Billy Goats make friends
2. Troll is lonely
3. Smallest Billy Goat falls off bridge
4. Troll saves him

Now try planning and writing your own story on a separate piece of paper.

Biography

Learning objective: To understand how to write a biography.

A book or a piece of writing that is an account of a person's life is called a biography.

A The paragraphs below are all from the biography of Roald Dahl. But they are all mixed up. Read them carefully and then write the order you think they go in.

Biography of Roald Dahl (1916–1990)

1. After school, he worked for the Shell Petroleum Company in Tanzania and in 1939, at the start of the Second World War, he joined the Royal Air Force.

2. He recovered and resumed duties in 1941 but then he started to suffer from headaches and blackouts.

3. Sadly, when he was just four, his seven-year-old sister died from appendicitis and a month later his father died from pneumonia.

4. He began writing in 1942 after being sent home from the army. His most popular children's books include *Charlie and the Chocolate Factory*, *James and the Giant Peach* and *The BFG*.

5. In 1940, Dahl was out on a mission when he was forced to make an emergency landing. Unluckily he hit a boulder and his plane crashed, fracturing his skull and his nose and temporarily blinding him.

6. Dahl married in 1953 and had five children.

7. Roald Dahl was born in Cardiff in 1916, the son of Norwegian parents.

I think that the paragraphs should go in the following order:

DEFINITION

timeline A line representing a period of time on which dates and events are marked.

B

Try and write a biography of a friend or relative. Before you start, use this space to draw out a timeline of their life. Include key events and the dates on which they happened. Write events above the line and dates below it.

Born

←——————————————————————————————→

Now write the biography in this space:

Persuasive writing

Learning objective: To learn to write persuasively.

Read the snippets of text taken from an advertising leaflet for Awesome Towers.

AWESOME TOWERS!

- Have you got what it takes to ride the biggest rollercoaster?
- Special holiday season tickets
- Park and ride
- Gift shop
- New this year!

AWESOME TOWERS!

- A fabulous day out for all the family!
- There's something for everyone...
- Fantastic fun-packed activities for all ages.
- Ride awesome rollercoasters.
- Watch spectacular live shows.
- Enjoy an excellent choice of cafes and restaurants.
- You're guaranteed to have fun!

Next time you visit an attraction pick up a leaflet and notice the way in which it is written.

A

Now write a leaflet advertising a major attraction near you.

Amazing day out! Come rain or shine!

Holiday discount prices

Buy one ticket, get one free!

How to write persuasive text:
- Use powerful adjectives, e.g. biggest, best, terrific, exciting, guaranteed, great.
- Use active verbs, e.g. enjoy, see, find, discover, watch, ride, go, eat.
- Speak to the reader, e.g. use the pronoun 'you'.

Writing a review

Learning objective: To write a review of a book, CD or film.

Read the book review below. Notice how it is set out under different headings.

Title: Kensuke's Kingdom
Author: Michael Morpurgo

Brief outline of the story
The story is about a boy called Michael and his family who set off to sail around the world. One stormy night Michael and his dog get washed overboard. They are rescued by Kensuke, an old man who lives on a desert island.

Strengths
I liked the way the author wrote about the friendship between Michael and Kensuke. It seemed very real, like a true story.

Weaknesses
I think it was sad at the end when Michael left the island. I usually prefer stories with happier endings. But if Michael had stayed his parents would have been unhappy.

Recommendation
This is a wonderful book. Children over 8 years old would enjoy it, as I have.

Score
9/10

DEFINITION
review An opinion or criticism of something.

58

Write a list of your top three books, CDs and films.

A

Write a review of a book, CD or film that you have enjoyed.

Title:
Author/artist:
Brief outline of the story

Strengths

Weaknesses

Recommendation

Score
/10

How to write a review:
• Give details about the book/CD/film.
• Write about the things you liked.
• Write about the things you didn't like.
• Give a recommendation: say who would enjoy it.

Answers

Page 6
A

spark, sparkle, sparkler
clear, cleared, clearly
bedroom, bedstead, bedtime
sign, signal, signature

Page 7
B

1. eight 2. hear 3. right 4. Would 5. Where 6. beach

Page 8
A

The month after April is May.
The shortest month is February.

Page 9
B

first, second, third, fourth, fifth, sixth, seventh, eighth, ninth, tenth

Page 10
A

sausages, cakes, drinks, books, horses, trees
dishes, kisses, foxes, lunches, buses, wishes, crosses
ponies, babies, stories, daisies, cherries, berries

Page 11
B

buds, millions, flowers, sandcastles, leaves, trees, snowmen
C

1. There are mice in the house! 2. There were only two loaves. 3. We saw geese
in the park.

Page 12
A

untie, unlock, unlike, unlikely, unable, unfair, undo, unlucky, unhappy, unhurt
I'm very unhappy with you. It's so unfair! I'm just unlucky!

Page 13
B

Tom and Jez went to see a remake of Monsters of the Deep. Writing about it
in a movie review for their school magazine, they said, "The monsters were
unrealistic and unimaginative really. There was lots of action but the plot was
disjointed and impossible to follow."
C

1. thoughtful 2. useless 3. hopeful 4. careful

Page 14
A

1. We'll have two cornets with raspberry sauce, a vanilla ice cream, a carton of
orange juice and a cup of tea please.
2. I'd like to order the tomato soup, an egg and cress sandwich, a banana
smoothie and a chocolate muffin please.
B

1. The cat ran up the stairs, down the corridor, through the classroom and into
Mrs Worgan's office!
2. Go right at the lights, turn right again at the T-junction, then first left.
3. The ball went straight down the course, over the rough, across the pond
and landed square on the green.

Page 15
C

1. Suddenly, all the lights went out!
2. "Aaaaaaaargh!" he cried.
3. Gina called out, "Hey, Tom!"
4. "What are 'gators?" she asked.
5. How do we know there's no life on Mars?
D

1. Tara cried, "Wait for me!"
2. "Do you think he's an elf?" said Taylor.
3. "Okay," said Sharon. "What's wrong?"
4. "Wow!" said Zac. "You're a genius!"

Page 16
A

can't, couldn't, shouldn't, we'll, they'll, where's, she's, they're
B

1. Ben's shoes 2. My friend's book 3. The dog's lead 4. Joe's car 5. The cat's
whiskers

Page 17
C

1. The girl's fish 2. The teacher's book 3. The family's television 4. The clown's

red nose 5. The babies' pram 6. The dolls' house 7. The children's drawings
8. The men's race

Page 18
A
The <u>flowers</u> were pretty.
<u>Zak</u> was asleep.
I live in <u>London</u>.
The <u>girls</u> laughed.
The <u>food</u> was delicious.
My <u>sister</u> has a <u>laptop</u>.
B
1. The flowers were pretty so I put <u>them</u> in a vase.
2. Zak was asleep so I didn't want to wake <u>him</u> up.
3. I like London because <u>it</u> has an interesting history.
4. The girls laughed because <u>they</u> thought it was funny.
5. Chris and I went swimming. <u>We</u> had a great time.

Page 19
C
<u>First</u>, after register we had a spelling test. <u>Then</u> we wrote animal poems.
<u>Before</u> lunch, we had a visitor. It was Mrs White. She'd brought her new baby
to show us. <u>After</u> lunch, we had games outside on the field. <u>But (or However)</u>
<u>suddenly</u> it started to rain and we had to run inside. <u>Next</u>, it was our science
lesson. <u>Finally</u>, just before home time we had a story.

Page 20
A
Colours: aqua, lemon, scarlet, violet, indigo. Sizes: huge, ginormous, miniscule,
average, narrow. Moods: sullen, raucous, excitable, angry, bored.
B
Possible answers:
1.   We had a <u>great</u> time.
2.   The pizza was <u>average.</u>
3.   The giant stomped his <u>huge</u> foot.
4.   It was a <u>hilarious</u> movie.

Page 21
C
black > white   scorching > freezing
bold > weak (or shy)   expensive > cheap
hazy > clear   popular > unpopular

hairy > bald (or hairless)   delicious > horrible (or disgusting)
unusual > common (or normal)   polite > rude
D
Possible answers:
1.   A <u>fierce, big</u> dog came bounding up to her.
2.   It was a <u>new/modern</u> table.
3.   It was an <u>easy</u> job.
4.   He was in a <u>sad/bad</u> mood.
5.   She went <u>white</u> when she saw him.

Page 22
A
1. found 2. chased 3. leaped 4. ate 5. skidded, crashed (two verbs).
B
Possible answers:
1. The girl <u>grabbed</u> the ice cream.
2. The red team <u>lost</u> the race!
3. The family <u>hated</u> camping.
4. The children <u>bought</u> a cake.
5. The boy <u>walked</u> across the road.

Page 23
C
1. The cat <u>purred</u> **softly**.
2. The giant <u>sneezed</u> **loudly**.
3. The man <u>drove</u> **quickly**.
4. The sun <u>beat</u> **fiercely**.
5. She <u>sang</u> **beautifully**.
D
Possible answers:
1. The teacher spoke <u>angrily</u>.
2. The boy <u>hurriedly</u> wrote his name.
3. The car <u>slowly</u> came to a halt.
4. The children played <u>happily</u>.
5. I sneezed <u>loudly</u>.

Page 24
A
1. It will rain on Wednesday.
2. It was sunny on Saturday.
3. Today it is Monday.

Answers

B

Past	Present	Future
It was hot	It is hot	It will be hot.
I was hot	I am hot	I will be hot.
He was hot.	He is hot	He will be hot.
We were hot.	We are hot.	We will be hot.
They were hot.	They are hot.	They will be hot.

Page 25
C

I am painting	I painted
I am jumping	I jumped
I am shopping	I shopped
I am skipping	I skipped

Page 27
B

REUSE AND RECYCLE
DANCING DOGS IN SCHOOL DRAMA
TWINS ARE A TERRIBLE TWOSOME
LOOK AFTER YOUR LONG LOCKS

Page 28
A

Volcanoes – NF
Primary Science – NF
Bedtime Stories – F
Poetry Collection – F
The Vikings – NF
Treasure Island – F

Page 29
B

A. Wizardy Woo B. Secrets and Spies C. Disappearing Worlds

C

Fiction: Wizardy Woo, Secrets and Spies
Non-fiction: Disappearing Worlds

Page 31
A

1. It is about the first day of the sales.

2. The customers are waiting outside.
3. She is nervous, dreading the opening.
4. They are 'like hyenas to a carcass'.
5. She is 'like an underwater swimmer moving against the current', and 'like a leaf carried in a storm'.
6. There will be chaos as the customers fight for bargains.
7. Any suitable title.

Page 32
A

A dog was hurrying home with a big bone that the butcher had given him. He growled at everyone who passed, worried that they might try to steal it from him. He planned to bury the bone in the garden and eat it later.

As he crossed a bridge over a stream, the dog happened to look down into the water. There he saw another dog with a much bigger bone. He didn't realize he was looking at his own reflection! He growled at the other dog and it growled back.

The greedy dog wanted that bone too, and he snapped at the dog in the water. But then his own big bone fell into the stream with a splash, and quickly sank out of sight. Then he realized how foolish he had been.

Page 33
B

1. He was hurrying to get home quickly before someone stole the bone from him.
2. The other dog growled back because it was just a reflection.
3. The dog learned that he had lost his bone because he was greedy.
4. b) it is foolish to be greedy.

Page 34-35
A

1. The extract tells us about the rats.
2. killed/cats/cradles; bit/babies.
3. vats, sprats, hats, chats, flats.
4. A ladle is a big spoon.
5. The apostrophe tells us that there is only one cook.
6. They all begin with an 's' sound. They also rhyme.
7. Hats worn on Sunday when going to church.
8. Sharps and flats are the sounds made by the rats squeaking and shrieking.

Page 36
A

1. The 'ee' or 'ea' sound is repeated three times.
2. Thinner rhymes with dinner. When we eat we usually grow fatter so growing thinner is a sign that the Vulture isn't well.
3. The poet is telling us that we shouldn't eat between meals.
4. It is not a serious poem but a fun or nonsense poem. The Vulture doesn't have a bald head and thin neck for the reasons given in the poem.

Page 37
B

1. Quickenham and sickenham are both made-up words, invented to rhyme with Twickenham.
2. She wore the boots for a short time before she took them off.

Page 39
A

"A new puppy!" Buster wailed. "After everything I've done for them."
"I knew you'd be upset," replied Sindy. "I said to our Mindy when I heard."
    "I take them for lovely walks, I eat up all their leftovers – even that takeaway muck they always dish out on a Friday... and this is the thanks I get!" said Buster.
    "You can choose your friends but you can't choose your owners," said Sindy, sympathetically.
    "What can they want a puppy for anyway?" cried Buster.
    "Well, puppies are cute," said Sindy.
    "Cute! Aren't I cute enough for them?" replied Buster.
    "Er ...," said Sindy.
    "Well, I'm telling you now," said Buster. "It's not getting its paws on my toys. I've buried them all!"

Page 40
A

1. She needs to leave at 2.45 pm in order to get to the appointment on time.
2. Becky's appointment is on Tuesday.
3. Mrs Kenwood apologises because Becky will miss lessons.
4. Becky will have to do her homework because Mrs Kenwood is going to collect it.

Page 41
B

1. The kitchen company's address is on the left.

2. Shoddy means careless and of poor quality.
3. Mrs Kenwood wants the company to put right these mistakes.
4. She is exasperated, disappointed and annoyed.

Page 42
A

1. You need a plastic bag, rolling pin, glass.
2. No there isn't enough for two glasses because the ingredients state 'serves 1'.
3. No, because the apple slices are for decoration only.
4. These words are verbs.
5. Any appropriate name.

Page 45
A

1. Phillip was angry because she was a Catholic and he was too.
2. 'This was the final straw' means that Phillip could not take any more.
3. The English ships could then be attacked on three sides.
4. The plan was to sail burning ships into them.
5. The English ships were smaller, faster, more agile and had better cannons.
6. The Armada was shipwrecked off the coast of Ireland and Scotland.
7. About 65 Spanish ships survived.
8. They all survived.

Page 48
A

1. A girl, about 9 years old. Someone who loves girlie things.
2. Princess, pretty, pink, pillows and purple; sequins and sparkled.
3. She was disappointed the ring wasn't pink.
4. The ring is important because we are told that it would change her world forever.

Page 50
A

1. Grandpa Bob is more likely to read books.
2. Auntie Deera is most likely to enjoy food because we are told she is plump.
3. (possible answer) Auntie Deera was tall and thin with a sharp, sullen face.
4. Zak is the youngest because the text implies that he is ten years old.
5. Charlie is probably a teenager.

Page 54
A 7, 3, 1, 5, 2, 4, 6

Index